an extract from

suhayl saadi's

the burning mirror

with an enthusiast's view

by catherine mcinerney

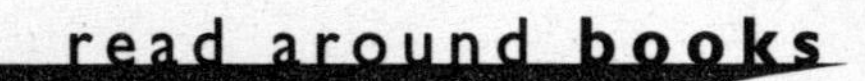

an extract from
suhayl saadi's

the burning mirror

with an enthusiast's view
by catherine mcinerney

2003

Published by
Scottish Book Trust
Scottish Book Centre
137 Dundee Street
Edinburgh EH11 1BG

Tel: 0131 229 3663

From April 2003 Scottish Book Trust will be moving its offices to Sandeman House, 55 High Street, Edinburgh EH1 1SR.

ISBN: 1 901077 09 8

Published with the support of the Scottish Arts Council National Lottery Fund and The Hugh Fraser Foundation.

The Burning Mirror is published by Polygon, an imprint of Birlinn Ltd
ISBN: 0 7486 6293 6

Series design by Caleb Rutherford eidetic
Printed in the UK by Cox & Wyman, Reading, Berkshire

contents

read around books

There is no shortage of fiction on the shelves of our bookshops – quite the opposite – but finding one that shouts out 'this is what you are looking for' is getting harder and harder as the number of books published goes up with each passing year. Too often we open a new book with expectation and enthusiasm only to discover disappointment and to struggle to get beyond page thirty. When we do find a book we really enjoy the urge is there to tell friends, colleagues and family to read it too in the hope that they will share our delight.

Read Around Books goes one step further and puts that enthusiasm down in black and white in the hope that many more readers will discover the joys of reading the very finest fiction that has emerged from Scotland over the last one hundred years. **This is a chance to sample before you borrow or buy**. Others have found these books before you, the writing held them spellbound and even when finished, these books would not let their readers go.

Each of the first twelve of these highly collectable little guide books promotes a work of fiction by a writer who lives in Scotland, was born in Scotland or who has been influenced by Scotland (our definition of Scottish is generous). Together they offer a marvellous introduction to the very best of Scottish writing from the twentieth and the first few years of the twenty-first centuries.

In each you will find a substantial extract, the enthusiast's view of the book, starting points for discussion for readers' groups, a short biographical piece about the author, and suggestions for similar reads which act as a further gateway to fine fiction.

Jan Rutherford
Series editor, 2003

the enthusiast

Catherine McInerney

Catherine McInerney is Literature Development Officer for Glasgow based at the Mitchell Library. She runs book groups and promotions in Glasgow libraries.

the enthusiast's view

The Burning Mirror
by Suhayl Saadi

Sometimes short stories can frustrate us, we get involved in the plot, feel like we've just got to know the characters, get intrigued, can't put the book down – then suddenly it's all over! We can feel abandoned and short-changed. Not so with Suhayl Saadi's debut collection. From Asian gangsta land and kebab houses in Govan to a journey into the mind of an 8,000-year-old genie and a love story set during the Balkan wars, these fabulous, experimental stories transport you and stretch your imagination.

This collection is an original, fresh and exciting book from a Glasgow based author of South Asian origin, who has also written poetry and novels. The stories are funny, clever and eclectic in theme ranging from childhood and coming of age, cultural identity in all its complexities to quests for spiritual and religious enlightenment. The individual stories are often thematically linked and there are two trilogies sewing the sequence together. The prose is distinctive, rich and often poetic with recurring images of heat and light.

Strands of Celtic mythology weave beautifully

throughout the tales merging myths with multi-cultural realities and many tongues speak a unique mixture of Punjabi, Scots and Scottish Gaelic.

In 'The Queens of Govan' we are introduced to Rubina who works in a Govan kebab shop and the complexities of her Scottish/Asian personality become apparent as the story unfolds.

> 'But she wis used to the double-life. At home, she wis totally, nauseatingly Mashriki, *Ah ho, God-be-with-you, behtiye khala ji*, while, outside, in the darkness of night or beneath the burnin sun of the parks, she would be rampant and would slip off towards dives which no one knew the names of.'

Issues surrounding identity are also at the forefront of 'The Dancers' where we meet Rosh, an Irish/Pakistani teenager:

> '*A mixed marriage*, everyone had called it, as though it had been a recipe or a cocktail. A Faisalabadi and a Belfast Catholic.' and 'When she felt Irish, she would be Róisín Dhu, the black rose, and when she thought that she was Faisalabadi, she would revert to Roshani, the ray of light. The split ran right inside her, it divided her into two, it apportioned her loyalties.'

In the award-winning story, 'Bandanna', gang member Salman is ashamed of his parents' occupation as Pakistani shopkeepers but a gang war experience leads him to a moment of truth and understanding in which he concludes '. . . that what he thought, felt, did, created during that minuscule pause in his fate might live beyond him, his family, the tribe to which he happened to belong, and that the only constant in the whole of Maxwell Park – the trees, the birds, the water, the kids – the only beat that pumped all other rhythms was the beat of love.'

He recognises the importance of religious tradition and the depths of his cultural heritage and '. . . he faced towards Gorbals Cross and began to pray.'

'Ninety-nine Kiss-o-grams' is about an older Sal from the earlier 'Bandanna' travelling to Pakistan to sell land left to him by his grandfather – he tells his story in a unique Scottish dialect. The complex emotions he experiences are apparent through the narrator's words: 'Nuthin wis certain here. Nuthin. Mibbee you were alive, mibbee you were deid. Mibbee there wis a God, mibbee there were ten thoosand. Everyone had a different version of everything, and nuhin wis written doon.'

At the heart of these stories is the notion of identity and belonging in all their complexities. They provide snapshots of Asian/Scottish contemporary urban culture in a lucid and realistic way.

'Imbolc', 'Samhain' and 'Lughnasadh' are a trilogy of stories drawing on Celtic mythology and are the names given in Scottish Celtic mythology for the cusps between the seasons.

'Imbolc' tells the story of a young man's sexual awakening on visiting the broch (fairy ring) in the coille (woods), the home of Big Bridie even though his granny had warned him never to go there.

In 'Samhain' – All Soul's Day – the protagonist, now an old dying man (the same young boy from Imbolc), looks back with regret at how he treated his wife and has ended up unhappy and alone.

'Lughnasadh' tells the story of four Irish students on a woodland walk who also discover a broch which unleashes their sexual inhibitions, culminating in a liberated naked romp in the river. This awakening leads to a shift in the relationships contained within the group and things can never be the same again:

> 'The boundaries between us had been erased, there in the pool, in the space that was Donal, and it could never be the same as before. The harmony of fine threads which we had danced upon was gone forever.'

The story ends on a note of hope, however, as the narrator seems to have achieved a sense of inner calm and enlightenment as a result of the experience.

In the second trilogy – 'The Naked Heart', 'The Ladder' and 'The Seventh Chamber', inspired by the lives and works of the Catholic mystical saints – the characters are non-immigrants. In the first story we meet John, riddled with guilt for the passion he feels for another church member Terri. In the second we learn that Terri has failed to find meaning in her relationship with her lover, Bernard, and in the concluding tale in the trilogy she has become a nun reflecting on the toils and tribulations of her life.

There is also a series of tales steeped in mysticism. 'Rabia' tells the story of a young man seeking a beautiful woman, Rabia, whom he encountered one morning at the market. This story is rich in beautiful poetic prose with lines such as '... the silent ice of the day stole through fissures in the skin, into the picot of the soul' and descriptions like 'The perfect dizzying curve of bird's flight from mountain top.'

The fairy-tale magic will transport you into the mountainous region near Kashmir. His journey though is also an analogy for an inner spiritual journey and we are left with the thought-provoking conclusion of the narrator:

> 'Perhaps, everyone has their own Rabia, their own yearning for that which they can never possess, something that is beyond matter, beyond themselves and the short span of their lives.'

'Brick' in which we can actually feel the brickmaker's burning desire is also a mystical tale set in Pakistan, rich in the country's mythical cultural legacy.

'The White Eagles' is a love story between a Serb and a Muslim in present day Bosnia, portraying the complexities of the political situation during the Balkans War. 'Everyone seemed to carry a sense of grievance, but no-one seemed really to know where it had come from.' Rich poetic prose is employed throughout the tale.

The final story 'Killing God' exposes the psyche of a jealous lover after a car accident: 'The whole chase had been a construct of hers, an anti-play designed by the wiggling toes of her soul to unravel the game which he had built around her.' We are left with the haunting suspicion that the narrator has murdered her rival …

This is just a taster of what's in store when you pick up the book. You will be intrigued and surprised by the variety and originality. The exploration of cultural customs and values, and the mixture of Punjabi and Scots employed to tell the tales is simply unlike anything you will ever have read or heard before.

The extract

The Burning Mirror

Ninety-nine Kiss-o-grams

He must've been mad tae have come here at this time ae year. Either that, or desperate. Forty-five degrees in the shade, and climbin. And that wis just the official reading, the wan they put in newspapers and atlases and tourist brochures – not that ony tourists ever came here, mind you . . .

Sal looked up and closed his eyes. Tried to blank oot the sun. But it wisnae like back hame. In the banjar zameene around Lahore, the sun was like God; it wis cursed by everyone, fae jagirdaar tae bhikari, fae mohlvi tae kunjari. He scuffed his foot aroon and stirred up the dirt, made it swirl intae the air so that he began tae cough. Deep, wrenchin coughs that were mair like big bokes. I'll choke on ma ane land, he thought and then he almost laughed through the tears, but it wis too hot tae laugh. Behind him sat the stupit car he'd used tae get here; it wis meant tae be *only twelve miles, bhai, fifteen at the most*, but it had taken longer than the drive from Glasgee tae Edinburgh on a rainy day, roadworks-an-aw. But then there wernae ony roadworks here. The roads never got repaired. Sometimes they nivir even got built. That wis the thing about Pakistan. You never knew anything, for certain. Temperature, direction, distance, the future . . . it wis aw up fur grabs. And money – well, money, that wis somehin else again. That wis why he wis oot here, Sal reminded himsel. Tae get money. And unlike maist ae whit went on here, it wisnae kala duhn he wis after. His dada had left aw his grandweans bits ae earth, thinkin that mibbee wan day, they would come back tae Pakistan and build hooses, all in a row just like in the auld days. His dada had worked like a dog tae get enough money tae buy these plots just ootside ae Lahore. It wis the sixties, and everyhin had been lookin up and he'd been tell't that the city would expand along wi the population and that in twenty years, the same bits ae wasteland would be worth *ten times more, bhai, ten times more*. Sal looked at the straggly, brown grass so unlike the bright-green mud-grass of Glasgee, and wondered how anyone could have believed that this land would ever be anything other than dry shit. Far away, a row of scorched trees quivered against the horizon, while to the east, in the direction of the Indian border, Sal thought he spotted a white-turbanned kisaan ploughing, behind a pair of bulls, through the yellow soil. He inhaled, slowly. This wis his country, the land ae his forefaithers and yet, the stink ae it sickened him tae his gut. That sweet smell ae rotting lemons, of uncollected rubbish, of unrepaired roads. Naa, he thought, and kicked the soil again, this isnae ma country. No ony mair. Mibbee, it nivir wis. He'd been tae Pakistan three or four times before, but nivir tae a shithole like this, and nivir in the depths ae summer, for God's sake!

The song he'd been playing, back in the car, seemed still to hover within the ripples of heat, the reel turning again and again as he walked slowly across the stretch of land. The groon wis hard, irregular, like wild-dog skulls, yet it crumbled into powder as his sandals touched the surface. Suddenly, a big, black bird swooped down and landed on a branch above his heid. He felt its eye slide along his spine. A perfect, black globe. Sal stopped walking, and tried tae stare back, but the light wis too strong, and his eyes began tae water. He wiped them wi the sleeve ae his kamise and removed a piece of paper from his shalvar pocket. Unfolded it. The sections came open uneasily and when they did, they left behind dirty-brown lines. Sal peered at the yellowed paper. The deeds. It had been written in Urdu script, and he couldnae read Urdu script. But right down at the dog-eared bottom, there were some letters in English which he'd tried tae make oot, all the way over, as he'd sat, bored and irritable, in the plane. They were probably meaningless, anyway. Most of the English here wis pretty meaningless. A kind ae jumbled-up mix ae auld colonial-speak and Amrikan Gangsta talk. His dada must have worn this piece ae paper like a lover as he'd sweatit thru the pissin rain an soor terraces ae Scola on his way tae makin it. Only he'd nivir really made it. No like the big Cash 'n' Carry Families, or the Restaurant Wallahs. Naw, his dada had ended up like a chhipkali in a bottle, always slidin up the glass walls and nivir really gettin onywhur. He felt like cryin as he remembered his dada's tired face, the cheeks sagging and full of lines, one crease for every year in exile. He focused down on the writing. *Half-an-acre*, it looked like, but you couldnae be sure. Somewhur between the burnin grass an the red sandstone, somewhur over those strange, blue seas, which they'd flash up alang wi the wee-whistle life jackets on the plane-flight, the exact measure of Sal's inheritance had got muddled, smudged, diluted. Sal jumped as the bird crowed through the heat. It had lost interest in him, and was gazing east, towards the land of Bhaarat. Now he'd come back to try and sell the land, to get what he could, and get oot again. But everything in Pakistan was cascading downwards like water from the Rawal Dam. The rupee had fallen from fifty-to-the-pound, to one hundred-and-thirteen (thirteen ... for luck? Sal had wondered); the only things which held their value in this country were truth and the loudspeakers outside mosques. Truth was priceless, and it wis everywhere. Look under any bush (burnin or not) and, there, you might find another truth. Sal thought that mibbee this wis because it wis so close tae Hindustan, wi its million gods crawlin aroon all over the place, lookin fur worship. His dada had listened to wan version of the truth when he'd been telt tae buy these plots; the city was goin tae spread like the music ae The Beatles over everything and, soon, the wee plots (the cotees all in a row, with the fair-skinned wives and the kala servants and the almost inaudible pulse of the air-conditioning) would be worth twenty times, *twenty times, bhai*, what they had been bought fur. And right enough, the city had expanded, aye, and laacs-upon-laacs ae cotees had sprung up like teeth all over the place but the problem wis, it had expanded in the wrang direction. It had gan north-east, not south-east and so his dada's plots had remained a wee wasteland. They might even have been shaam laat e shair, common land of the city, and then they would not have been his dada's, after aw. Nuthin wis certain here. Nuthin. Mibbee you were alive, mibbee you were deid. Mibbee there wis a God, mibbee there were ten thoosand. Everyone had a different version of everything, and nuhin wis written doon. Or if it had been, then it would have got washed away in the waters of the Rawal Dam, the night they had burst through stane and concrete and flooded the valley of Punjab, killing thousands. Or mibbee that hasnae happened yet, Sal thought. It wis hard tae be sure. He'd not got very far, trying tae sell the plot; prices were dirt-low and almost no one wis buying land. Anyone who wis anyone wis tryin tae put money intae foreign banks, or tae get oot themselves. No one wanted land in a country that wis goin tae the dogs and the sand. He spat, and his spittle landed on a hump of yellow earth where it lay but did not dissolve. Sal bent down and stared into the dome of the blob. He'd often wondered what he would do with the money. It wisnae gonna be a fortune. It might buy the wheel-trims ae a Merc; or else, a wide-screen TV so that his behene could sit an watch stupit Bombay filmi films. Three hours ae *rim-jim* and *roo-roo* and violins that screeched around yer skull. Or mibbee he would invest it in the shop. Turn it fae a cornershop intae a boutique like the wan his bitch cousin hud on Cathcart Road. Get merrit, huv a family. Naw. He had other dreams for his dada's land. In Sal's dream, the money, coverted like Sal, from rupees intae pounds, would go tae buy a kiss-o-gram. Or, to be mair precise, ninety-nine kiss-o-grams. All blond and bikini'd and stonin in a circle aroon him, and smilin at him wi thur thick, red lips . . . he saw himsel surroondit by them, their wee white breasts pushin intae his broon face, fillin his mooth, his body so that he couldnae breathe fur the whiteness. So that he could become invisible. But that wis jist a dream. In Scola, there wus nae room fur dreams; in Pakistan, dreams were all there wus. He scrunched up the deed and went to put it back in his pocket. Felt it slip from his hand. He bent down to pick it up but couldn't see where it had gone. There wis a clump ae grass, jis beneath his foot, but it wasnae in there. He swore aloud, but his voice was immediately swallowed up in the molten air, and, for the first time, Sal felt scared. He felt sweat spike along the line of his spine. His hair lay matted, dank over his scalp. He shouldnae huv driven oot here on his ane. The thought occurred to him that perhaps the deed might've slipped somehow (anything was possible) into the lining of his shalvar. He ran his hands over the smooth, white cotton, rapidly at first but then slowly, carefully as he held his breath and felt the heat enter him and swell in his chest. *Forty-six degrees, forty-seven . . .*

It wasn't there. It wasn't on the ground either and the earth all just looked the same. It wisnae like Scola, wi aw its shades like the different malts; naw, from the plane, Pakistan wis jis wan, scorched broon. Suddenly he longed for the cool spaces ae Scola, the feel ae the rain on his back. He rummaged aroon wi the tip ae his shoe, but all he got wis mair dust. There wouldn't be another copy – God knew when and where his dada had got it from and onyway nothing would ever huv been written down, and if it had been, then it would be a lie. Truth was held in the air like the waves of heat that burned his skin. He felt the glare of the bird on the back of his neck but fought the temptation to look back. He got down on his hands and knees and began to rummage his palms through the dry soil. The dust made him sneeze, and his eyes began to water, but he took no notice, and let the tears drip silently on to the earth. The soil tasted bitter, like ajwain. Sal had heard that farmers sometimes tasted the soil of their fields, to test its quality. Eejeuts. His breath burned the lining of his throat and he needed a drink. There was boiled water in the car, but Sal didnae dare leave the plot. His grandfather hud sweatit for this land and in the end, he hud died fur it and he wisnae goin tae jis let it slip away so that some fat zamindaar could come and swallow it up, for nothin. A year back, his papa hud ran aff wi a goree and the whole family had been disgraced (as a result of this, his maa had developed five thoosand illnesses, all of which seemed tae afflict her concurrently, and his dada had gan tae his grave while watchin Madubala fling herself from the stone parapet in the video of the film, *Mahal*). Now Sal wis the man and, being the eldest, it wis up tae him tae save at least somehin ae the family's honour; he hud tae get a guid, or at the very least a reasonably pukka, price for this piece ae pure yellow shite and he couldnae go hame, empty-handed, he just couldnae . . .

There wis nae breeze, but Sal thought he felt wan. He paused for a moment. His face wis covered in dust, his clothes were no longer white, but had acquired the dun chamois in which most Pakistanis over here seemed to dress. His hair fell across his eyes, and he brushed it back wi his hond but it jis fell forwards again. His mother had told him (countless times) tae get it cut *and why don't you try to look like a respectable bundha*? So he'd got fed up and, wan day, he'd gan oot and got it cut. A Number Wan. After that, she'd thrown her honds up intae the air and screamed, *Hai-hai!* and had taken to her bed for two days. You couldnae please them, no matter what you did. He hated his faither fur what he had done, but he hated him mair because he'd landed Sal right in it. Now Sal wis it. All eyes were on him, and he had tae succeed, or else he might as weil be deid. Mibbee he wuid be better aaf deid; at least then, he would be a hero, or a martyr or, at the very least, someone not tae be spoken ill of. An image of the goree, bein screwed by his faither flashed intae his mind. He pushed it away. In the past, they'd sometimes talked aboot the men who'd been seen hauding honds wi mini-skirtit gorees an walkin doon the street. And he'd despised those men and yet, at the same time, he'd wantit tae be wan ae them. Tae huv his ane long-legged, thin-waisted goree tae wave like a white flag at the world. And then his faither had gone an done that, and made it impossible fur Sal. Now, he would nivir be able tae surrender. Sal wus deid, right enough, deid an buried beneath the big, wet stanes ae Albert Drive. Beneath the big, white sky. He forced his mind back tae the deed, the plot, his honour. He had the insane thought of removing his shalvar and turning it inside-out to search for the piece ae paper. He looked around. There wis no one about. The peasant whom he had spotted earlier had vanished. He was far from anywhere. It would take only a few seconds. And onyway, time here wis different. Everything around him had grown silent. Or mibbee it had always been like that, he wisnae sure. He got down on his hands and knees and began to search for the deed. He felt the cotton ae his claes stick tae his back like a lizard skin. After a while, he stopped and rolled over.

Everything looked different. The sky was everywhere, and its blueness had faded into a shimmering silver. The bird was no longer in the tree, but was scarpering along the ground. Every so often, its head would flick down and then up, and every time this happened, its beak would emerge empty, black. It seemed a lot smaller than before, its stupit wee deformed twig legs were like those of an auld wummin. It'll no find ony worms here, he thought. Sal began to feel uncomfortable. He felt as though he was sinking into the soil. His nails were all smashed and blood had begun to trickle from the end of his thumb. Slowly, he got up. The bird had disappeared. You couldnae even trust yer ane eyes. He removed his sandals and set them neatly aside. Spat again, to clear the dust from his mouth. He looked around, just tae check, and in one smooth movement, he slipped the elastic of his shalvar down and over his feet and stepped awkwardly out of it. He lifted it up, and shook the cloth so that a fine dust flew everywhere. Nothing. He turned it inside-out and shook it again but still, nothing. The dust smelt ae bhang. The whole country's gan tae pot, Sal thought, and then he laughed. He was about to put the shalvar back on, when the thought occurred to him that the paper might somehow have fallen, not into his shalvar but into his kamise. He threw the shalvar down on to the ground and slipped the long shirt up, over his head. The heat scalded his back, he could feel the cells begin to fry, one by one. His head felt like it was goin tae burst and his breath was coming in short rasps. *Forty-nine degrees, fifty* ... He shook out the kamise but it, too, was empty. Exasperated, Sal tossed it aside and glared up at the sky which had become so bright, it held no colour at all. It was as though the sun had exploded and filled the entire sky with its burning substance. He tried to swear, but his mouth was parched, and no words came. He shook his fist at the sun, or God, or truth or whatever was up there. He fell to his knees and began frantically to search for the piece of paper which had hauled him across five thousand miles and three generations to the plot which he an his dada, both, had dreamt of and, as he churned up the earth, the dust swirled into the air so that there, in the land that was his by right of inheritance, he had, at last, become invisible.

And because of the clouds of ochre dust which surrounded him, Sal did not see the bird up in the tree as it flapped its wings, twice, and took off into the burning sky.

Imbolc

Jis beyond the leathad which fell behind our hoose, there wis a wee coille. It wis aw the kina trees that would shed their leaves in the autumn and, at that time, you could see richt through them and they seemed aw lighted up and open. But it wisnae autumn, it wis spring and the leaves were sproutin all over the place like the saft wee lambs up on the moor. I wisnae supposed tae venture onywhur close tae the coille, for ma grannie said thur wur wild deer that roamed aboot in it and that they wud attack onyone who went near thur young, especially in spring. Some hings were oota boonds and no jis places. Fowk an tids were beyond the pale as weil. Like Big Bridie fae the craft across the wa'ar. Ah wisnae allowed tae talk aboot her, no even tae mention her name if Grannie wis payin heed. It wisnae jis ma grannie, aw the grannies, the auld wumin, they never talked aboot her save the odd comment like *An Diabhal toirt leis i!* or other such curses. Aye. Big Bridie wis the scorn o the glen. We lads wur aw feart ae her, ah don't know how. We never looked her in the ee when she passed us on the path. Naw, no wi her rid rid locks. We shook oor heids jis as oor grannies did. Naw, naw, *She'll go tae the divil, aye*, her n her callants, her big bothy boys aye n there wur feck o them tae. Big Bridie wuid jis toss back her rid heid and laugh that boomin laugh ae hers and the soon ae it wud echo through the glen and set aw the grannies fae wan end tae th'other tae shakin thur heids and tut-tuttin and missin the slip-stitches in thur knittin.

Weel, ah must've been aleeven or twalt at the time, ah canny remember rightly since as the oors kinda went aw funny aroon then. It wis a gae spring morn an ah wis playin wi ma baw ootside ma grannie's gate (she widnae let me play in the garden cause ah knacked her floors, which she wis gae pruidae, aye she used tae win local competitions, so she did, wi her floors the brichtest an her kails the biggest in the glen ah weil remember ma Grannie Urquart stonin haudin a kail in yan hond ae a great big tulip in th'other an that wis before yer fertilisers it wis aw crap then ah mean guid crap, the crap o the coos an the sheep and sometimes, aye sometimes thur's nae shame in admittin it, the kak e human bains as weil). Onyhow, ah wis kickin ma baw aboot in the lang, wild gress o the beinn when aw ae a sudden this notion comes intae ma heid tae venture doon intae the coille. Ah dinnae know how it came intae ma heid ah dinnae know but it did, mibbee it wis the guid fowk, mibbee, ah couldnae say no noo ah couldnae. So kickin ma wee baw a wee bit further every time jis a wee bit further, aw the while keepin a gae close ee on the kitchen ae the craft in case ma grannie might spie me an caw me back intae the hoose an it wud be nae supper and early tae bed. It's nae that ah wantit tae begowk ma guid grannie. It wis jis that ah wis a wee boy and ah wis up tae wee boy's swicks. So there ah wis, movin towards the coille, an neither mon nor beast nearby no even the shepies no even the troddles ae sheep no even the braith ae a sheep let alane that ae a carle. Weil, ah got tae the wood's edge and paused. Jis fur a moment, jis enough to feel timorsome. But ah wisnae gan tae go back noo, no noo ah wisnae so ah gathert up ma baw ma freen aw yella wi green stripes it wis an ah walked like a mon straucht intae the coille.

The trees wur gae heich, the cabers, the blae lift. An then thur wur some which wur jis scrunts like they'd jis stapped growin, they wur stunted, like grumphie aud carles. But the shanks wur no like that. They wur aw smilin a bit like ma gran. Aud, but freendlie. Aye. An thur leaves wur sproutin oot in aw directions, saft, green fingers shakin honds wi me aye like wan wean tae another. Ah fain likt the touch o those young leaves all over ma shooders, ma back aye an ah took aff ma shaes an trod wi ma bar fit alang the saft grun. Aye, it wis saft wi aud leaves, last year's faw an the faw ae the year afore and the wan afore that. In fact the mair ah thocht on't, the mair ah realised that ah wis plowterin through history. Mibbee somewhur beneath ma fit thur lay Saint Brendan's Island as ah'd been tailt by ma grannie. That's whur aw the magic came fae. It didnae occur tae me that, come autumn, all those young leaves would be drappin aaf nineteen-tae-the-dozen. It didnae occur tae me then but it does noo, aye so it does. Ah couldnae see through tae th'other side so ah wuntit tae go through tae th'other side it's gae strynge how that happens tae a wean and it still happens tae the mon because we never really grow up no really no like those bastarts ye see in the stories ah mean the tippie stories whur they grow tae a resolution, naw that nivir happens in real life. Nivir.

Ah looked back tae see if ah could spot ma grannie's hoose ma hoose whur ah'd been born an raised and thur wis jis me'n ma grannie, ma granpa hovin been kilt in the War ah dinnae remember which war but it wis some big stour or other. Ma maw... och, nivir mind aboot that. Ah looked back an couldnae see ocht. A shither ran through ma body an ah felt like greetin but ah didnae cause ah knew it wuid do nae guid. It nivir did. Ah wis treadin through the coille aw careful like, wan foot after the other, balancin wi ma baw tucked alow ma car airm an ma richt aw balancin like in the circus since the grun wis aw bumpy what wi stanes an tufts ae grass an the like. Aye, an then ah saw a pad, a wee road, weil it wis mair like a track, a trinkit track, aw ruts an bits ae heather comin awa aw over wi iteodha an hawthorne aw towerin over reachin doon so low that, wean as ah wis, ah hud tae bow ma heid as ah walked. The passage wis narra an low jis like two honds perched in prayer like the minister in the kirk. But this wis nae kirk. Aw ae a sudden, ah came across a stane. A big, tall stane. Moss wis growin all over it which made it seem gae ault. Near wan side ae the stane wis a hole, jis big enough tae fit ma hond and nae mair. It ran richt through the stane, richt through. Ah stretched ma airms roon the clach chaol, àrd so that ma lisk wis pressin up agin the cool rock and ah wis jis able tae haud honds through the hole. It wis gae strange, but ah didnae want tae let go, ah felt as if it wis some other body's hond ah wis claspin on th'other side ae the stonin stane. Ah wis feart but ah wis also gae blithe an a terrible drùis seemed tae come fae the big, cauld stane and tae rise up through ma wee stanes and alang ma tadger, the insides ae ma thighs, ma belly, ma back, richt the way up tae ma heid which began poundin it wis like Cailleach a' Gheamhraidh bangin her hammer on the grun tae steek the earth fur the wold month aye, thump-thump-thump ma heid pounded wi the beat ae ma hairt the blood bellowin in ma lugs O Goad whit wis this the sow-thistles at the base ae the stane wur stingin ma bare legs but ah didnae care ah didnae care it made the torrent intae wan, flowin richt through ma body, fae ma tadger, which wis sprung like the cabers up above, aw the way doon tae ma taes an aw the way up tae ma tap. An in ma mind wis a picture, a movin picture ae Big Bridie, her ae the craft across the wa'ar, her wi the big breists tae big fur hur ane guid they said and her big milky thighs and she wis movin an smilin and ah wis movin an smilin there agin the stane wi ma ees shut tight an ma back straicht as a silver tree. O Goad O Goad O Goad an the rock wis rippin through ma breeks but ah didnae care naw ah didnae cause ah always ae fancied Big Bridie so did aw the boays thereaboots but ma grannie an they said she wis gan wi aw kinds ae billies ten or mair years awder an her aye in the fields and clais an by the baunk ae the burns a' beucaich aw fuck an ah wantit Big Bridie ah wantit her hot, braw thighs tae clasp aroon ma back ah wantit her tae ram me aye ah did jis like she rammed them big carles in thur creakin bothies aifter the coos hud been taken hame tae the coo-shed. An the stonin stane wis Bridie wi her rid hair jis like mine an she wis smilin at me, me, wee Scott who wis jis ootae his grannie's braw airms cause his maa'd gan aff wi some gallus Sasunnach so his grannie had telt him. An he couldnae even remember her face naw, no even whun he wis fawin asleep no even whun he wis hingin, no even whun he wis feelin like greetin but he didnae care cause it nivir did ony guid o fuck naw naw naw and the stane wis his maa and the stane wis Big Bridie an the stane wis his maa an the stane wis Big Bridie the dun coo wi her lang white wand touchin the hard earth touchin me makin ma body feel sae guid sae bloody guid an the siol flowin freely like the shairp whistle o the gawden and green plover, heavin an lyin, lyin an heavin in the deid calm o the coille wi the thistles an dockins aw aroon ma fit, the sow-thistle wi its thick white juice and ah wis Goad, Goad forgive me, ah wis Goad. An ah nivir noticed, as ah washed mysel in the wee alltan nearby that the whole coille wis growin aroon an awd broch, an awd faery broch aye an that wis why ma grannie hud said ah should nivir go there.

But she wis wrang, ma auld grannie, she wis wrang.

glossary

ajwain	a bitter-tasting spice
banjar zameene	wastelands, scrublands
bhang	marijuana
behene	sisters or female relatives
bhikari	beggar
bundha	man
Cailleach a' Gheamhraidh	the Old Woman of the Winter
carle	young man
chhipkali	lizard
clach chaol, àrd	thin, high stone
coille	forest, wood
cotee	house
drùis	lust
grumphie	a pig, a grumbler
iteodha	hemlock
jagirdaar	big landowner in Punjabi
kala duhn	'black money', ie money obtained or converted via the black market
kisaan	peasant / peasants
kunjari	whore
laacs	hundreds of thousands

leathad	slope / side of a hill
lisk	groin
mohlvi	Muslim 'priest'
shalvar	loose, baggy trousers worn by Punjabi men and women
shanks	stems of trees
siol	seed, spawn, semen
tippie	fashionable
trinkit	rutted
troddles	sheep-dung
zamindaar	Punjabi landowner

about the **author**

Suhayl Saadi

Suhayl Saadi is a widely-published poet and short story writer of South Asian origin. He has won numerous awards including second prize in the Macallan/*Scotland on Sunday* short story competition for his story 'Ninety-nine Kiss-o-grams', published in *The Burning Mirror. The Burning Mirror* was shortlisted for the Saltire Society First Book award in 2001. His novel, *Kings of the Dark House* is due out in 2003.

Suhayl was born in Yorkshire and moved to Scotland when he was four years old. In 2000 he founded the innovative Pollokshields multi-ethnic writers' group with a grant from the Millennium Awards scheme and until recently was co-ordinator of that group which is still running. He is a practising GP and has won a patient-nominated Health Council award. Suhayl lives in Glasgow with his wife and young daughter. He spends a lot of time standing on street corners . . .

Catherine McInerney met Suhayl in a coffee-house on Byres Road recently. Here are some of the questions she asked him.

How would you describe your book to a new reader?

I would describe the work as eclectic and something that tries to stretch the reader's imagination – in the same way that when I write it stretches *my* imagination. I try to capture elements of the unexpected, for example, the urban realist technique cropping up in a different and unexpected environment.

What is the significance of the book's title?

The title *The Burning Mirror* refers to the multi-faceted nature of the mirror-window. There is the Lewis Carroll association, the entry point into the surreal and the fantastic and there is also the Sufi expression that 'all things are by their opposite known'. By the use of the word 'burning' as an adverb the mirror becomes an instrument, a weapon even, of fire.

What other short story collections would you recommend to readers?

I would recommend Juan Rulfo's *Pedro Paremo, The Garden of Secrets* by Juan Goytisolo and *This Other Salt* by Aamer Hussein.

discussion **points**

1. The short story genre

2. Cultural Values and Customs

3. Identity and Belonging

4. Family Relationships

5. Language

press quotes

'... There is a rhythm and blending of languages that is uniquely Scots-Asian ... I am not sure that we've ever heard such a deft British-Asian voice before.'
– Chris Dolan

'Suhayl Saadi's debut collection of short stories is a small treasure. His is such a unique voice in Scottish literature it is impossible not to get swept up in his many experiments with form and content ... Funny, clever and complex, his Scots Asian voice is very fresh, and reminiscent of masters like Salman Rushdie and Alan Warner and, on this evidence, Saadi may soon be at the point of having few contemporary rivals.
– *The List*

'The stories ... are similarly eclectic in theme, from a harassed woman in a Govan kebab shop to the mind of an 8,000-year-old genie, a wartime Bosnian love story to one about bonded workers in a Pakistani brick-making village ... The vibrancy of Saadi's writing is itself a burning mirror to that of Scottish writing as a whole.'
– *Scotsman*

'The author skilfully takes the reader on a magic carpet that touches down in unlikely places, touching subjects that you wouldn't think of – a perfect example being a love story set during the Balkans War. Saadi's writing is like a simple key that unlocks a Pandora's box with stories that are surreal and simple standing side-by-side. If... there were less slang in some of the stories, this would have been one of the books of the year.'

– *Eastern Eye*

'Saadi writes with an economy of style and sharply observed details which evoke urban Scotland as vividly as rural Pakistan, and a humour as bitter as the dusty earth.'

– Sheena Mackay

similar **reads**

Stone Garden and Other Stories by Alan Spence
(Orion; ISBN: 1897580630)
Central to this exquisite collection from one of Scotland's greatest contemporary writers is the notion of quest – both emotional and spiritual. The search for truth and inner peace is at the core of the journey each character embarks upon.

Walking the Dog by Bernard MacLaverty
(Penguin Books; ISBN: 0140236368)
A very memorable collection from a well-loved Irish writer whose characters you feel you really know by the end of the book. The stories evoke real life experiences of ordinary people living in Northern Ireland against a backdrop of political unease.

Interpreter of Maladies by Jhumpa Lahira
(Flamingo; ISBN: 0006551793)
This is Lahira's first collection of short stories written mainly from an Indian Bengali perspective. Cultural values and customs are a central thread throughout the stories covering topics from childbirth, grief and mourning, to homesickness and survival.

The Elephant Vanishes by Haruki Marukami

(Vintage; ISBN: 0099448750)

A hilarious and magical collection of enthralling, surreal tales from a contemporary Japanese writer. The title takes its name from a haunting, funny and thought-provoking story about an elephant that simply disappears!

Dubliners by James Joyce

(Penguin Books; ISBN: 0141182458)

A read through these twelve short stories – all set in Dublin though depicting very different yet fascinating characters – will transform and excite you! Each story is an individual masterpiece.

Free Love and Other Stories by Ali Smith

(Virago Press; ISBN: 1860495842)

An intriguing collection from a twice Scottish Arts Council Book Award winner. Central to the core of these short stories are themes of desire, sexual ambiguity and the unexpectedness of life and we are left with a warm, hopeful sense of how love really can conquer all.

competition

Your chance to win ten contemporary works of fiction signed by their authors.

The *Read Around Books* series was developed by Scottish Book Trust to encourage readers to widen their reading interests and discover writers they had never tried before. Has it been a success? We want to hear from you. Tell us if you have enjoyed this little series or not and if you did, do you have any suggestions for authors who should be included in the series in the future.

Writer to us now with the following information:

Name and address
Email address
Are you a member of a readers' group?
Name of reader's group

Send us the information above and we will enter you into our prize draw to be drawn on 22 August 2003.

Send to:
RAB Draw
Scottish Book Trust
137 Dundee Street
Edinburgh EH11 1BG

scottish book trust

What is Scottish Book Trust?

Scottish Book Trust exists to serve readers and writers in Scotland. We work to ensure that everyone has access to good books, and to related resources and opportunities.

We do this in a number of ways:

- By operating the Writers in Scotland Scheme, which funds over 1,400 visits a year by Scottish writers to a variety of institutions and groups
- By supporting Scottish writing through a programme of professional training opportunities for writers
- By publishing a wide variety of resources and leaflets to support readership
- By promoting initiatives such as National Poetry Day and World Book Day
- And through our Book Information Service, providing free advice and support to readers and writers, and the general public.

For more information please visit
www.scottishbooktrust.com

titles **in the series**

Available in the Read Around Books series

Iain Crichton Smith's *Murdo: The Life and Works,* by Douglas Gifford

Meaghan Delahunt's *In The Blue House,* by Gavin Wallace

Michel Faber's *Under the Skin,* by Mary Firth

Jonathan Falla's *Blue Poppies,* by Rosemary Goring

Janice Galloway's *Clara,* by David Robinson

Andrew Greig's *That Summer,* by Alan Taylor

Anne MacLeod's *The Dark Ship,* by Lindsey Fraser

Maggie O'Farrell's *After You'd Gone,* by Rosemary Goring

Suhayl Saadi's *The Burning Mirror,* by Catherine McInerney

Ali Smith's *Hotel World,* by Kathryn Ross

Muriel Spark's *The Comforters,* by Alan Taylor

Alexander Trocchi's *Young Adam,* by Gillian Mackay